STORIES FROM India

Folklore of the World

Each of the Folklore of the World Books contains carefully selected myths and folktales most representative of a single country. These books will help children to understand people in other lands and will help them to develop an appreciation for their customs and culture. Peace for the world can come only through the spreading of this understanding and appreciation.

The Folklore Books are the third step in the Dolch program, *Steps to a Lifetime Reading Habit.* The series on these graded steps, starting with the most elementary, are: the First Reading Books, the Basic Vocabulary Books, the Folklore of the World Books, and the Pleasure Reading Books.

Folklore Books are prepared under the direction of Edward W. Dolch, formerly Professor of Education, University of Illinois. In all the series, emphasis is placed on good storytelling and literary quality, as well as on simplicity of vocabulary.

Books in this series are (to date):

Stories from Alaska
Stories from Canada
Stories from France
Stories from Hawaii
Stories from India
Stories from Italy
Stories from Japan
Stories from Mexico
Stories from Old China
Stories from Old Egypt
Stories from Old Russia
Stories from Spain

STORIES FROM India

Folklore of the World

by EDWARD W. DOLCH
and MARGUERITE P. DOLCH

illustrated by
GORDON LAITE

GARRARD PUBLISHING COMPANY
CHAMPAIGN, ILLINOIS

Library of Congress No.: 61-5487

MANUFACTURED IN THE UNITED STATES OF AMERICA

Foreword

Many of the stories from India go back into the distant ages before writing had been invented or books of any kind were made. In those days, the people gathered around the "storyteller" in the evening to listen for hours to his tales. In many parts of India, they still gather to listen to the same stories.

Though modern India is a country of many languages and many cultures, it is surprising that so many of the same stories are found among widely different peoples in distant parts of that great land. Perhaps this is true because, over so long a time, the stories have been passed from one people to another, and from one language to another.

This selection of stories from the great multitude of the folk stories of India will give some idea of the variety in the folklore and some idea of the life of the people. There are stories of the familiar animals, the ox, the monkey, the rabbit, the donkey, the elephant. There are stories of the life of the villages. There are stories of the life of the palaces of the kings or rajahs. And there are stories of the gods. All these are part of the great whole that we call India.

If these stories are interesting, if they give some taste of the magic of the Indian folk story, the reader will want to go to the many volumes of Indian folklore for further enjoyment.

E. W. Dolch

Santa Barbara, Calif.

Contents

The Four Friends

Once upon a time, a Mouse, and a Crow, and a Turtle and a Deer were friends. They lived in the forest near a lake. Every day the four friends met and told each other stories.

But one day Deer did not come. Mouse and Crow and Turtle were very much worried.

"I saw Hunter in the forest this morning," said Crow. "I am afraid some harm has come to Deer."

"Fly over the forest, Friend Crow," said Mouse, "and see if you can find Friend Deer."

Crow flew over the forest. When he came to the lake, he found Deer caught in a trap made of ropes.

"Friend Deer," said Crow, "how did you get caught in that trap?"

"I came down to the lake to get a drink. I did not see the trap in the grass," said Deer.

"Hunter will surely kill you," said Crow.

"Give my love to Friend Mouse and Friend Turtle," said Deer. "Tell them I am remembering all the stories that they told to me."

Crow went and told Mouse and Turtle what had happened to Deer.

"We must not let Hunter kill

Deer," said Mouse. "I will go and bite the ropes. I will free Deer."

Mouse ran to where Deer was caught in the trap of ropes. Mouse cut the ropes with his teeth.

"Oh, thank you, my good Friend," said Deer. "Now we must get away from here."

Then who should they see in the grass but Turtle.

"Why did you come here, Friend Turtle?" cried Deer.

"I was worried about you," said Turtle.

"If Hunter comes," said Deer, "Crow can fly away. Mouse can

hide in the grass. I can run away fast. But you cannot run fast."

Just then Hunter, with his bow and arrows, came through the forest. He was very much surprised to see the ropes of his trap all cut. But Hunter saw Turtle.

"A turtle is better than nothing," said Hunter.

Hunter tied Turtle's feet with a rope. Then he picked up Turtle and started home.

Now Mouse and Crow and Deer were much worried.

"Poor Turtle was our friend," said Deer, "Now Hunter is going to kill him."

"We can save Turtle," said Mouse. "Friend Deer, you must run ahead of Hunter without letting him see you. Then drop down in the grass as if you were dead. Friend Crow, you must sit on Friend Deer's head. Hunter will think that Friend Deer is dead. Then he will put Friend Turtle down and go to get Deer. I will at once cut the rope from Turtle's feet."

It happened just as Mouse had said.

Hunter saw what he thought was a dead deer. He put Turtle down and ran to get the deer.

Then Mouse cut with his teeth the ropes that tied Turtle's feet.

As soon as Hunter was near to the deer in the grass, Crow flew away and Deer got up and ran into the forest.

"There is some magic here," said Hunter to himself.

Then Hunter went back to get Turtle but he found him gone.

"There is some great magic here," cried Hunter, and he ran out of the forest as fast as he could go.

The four friends sat together in the forest by the lake.

"It is good to have friends," said Mouse.

"Yes," said Deer, "Hunter would have killed me if I had not had good friends."

"Yes," said Turtle, "this very night, I would have been made into turtle soup if I had not had good friends."

"Yes. Yes," said Crow. "Good friends are the best thing the gods can give to animals or to man.

The Magic Pot

There was once a poor Brahman who had a wife and four children. The Brahman was a good man who said his prayers and washed his hands before eating. But the Brahman was very poor.

The wife and the four children were often hungry. The Brahman was very sad.

One day he went away from his village. He went into a dark forest. There he prayed to the goddess Durga.

Durga, Durga, Durga.
I pray to you each day.
For myself, I ask nothing.
But you have given me
  a wife and four children.
My children are hungry.
Help them, I pray.

The goddess Durga heard the prayer of the poor Brahman. She was sorry for him. She appeared before him in the dark forest.

"Brahman, I have heard your prayers. Now I bring to you a magic pot. When you turn this pot upside down, a stream of cooked rice will fall from it. If you take good care of the pot, you and your wife and your children will never be hungry again."

The Brahman bowed to the ground before the goddess. When he looked up, she was gone. But right before him was an old cooking pot. He picked up the pot and hurried out of the forest.

"I will stop and see what the pot will do," said the Brahman to himself. So he stopped and turned the pot upside down.

A stream of cooked rice came out of the pot. When the pot was turned right side up, the stream of cooked rice stopped.

The Brahman would have liked

to eat the rice. But a good Brahman does not eat before he says his prayers and washes his hands. So the Brahman tied the rice in a cloth and went on his way. He was a very happy man.

Soon the Brahman came to an inn. There was a pool of water beside the inn where he could wash his hands. As the Brahman stopped, the Innkeeper came out and spoke to him.

The Brahman said to the Innkeeper, "Take good care of my cooking pot while I wash my hands in the pool and say my prayers to the goddess Durga. Be sure to take very good care of my cooking pot."

When the Brahman had gone to wash, the Innkeeper began to wonder why he was to take good care of an old cooking pot. It looked like any other old cooking pot. He picked it up and looked inside, but there was nothing inside the pot. He turned the pot around and around. Then to look at the bottom, he turned it upside down.

Suddenly a stream of cooked rice came out of the pot.

"This is a magic pot," cried the Innkeeper. "I will give the

Brahman one of my old cooking pots and I will keep this magic pot for myself."

When the Brahman had said his prayers and washed his hands, he ate the rice that he had tied in the cloth. Then he went to the Innkeeper and asked for his cooking pot.

"Here is the cooking pot," said the Innkeeper. "I have taken very good care of your cooking pot."

The Brahman hurried home to show the magic pot to his wife.

"My good wife," cried the Brahman, when he got to his hut. "You and the children will never be hungry again. I have a magic pot which was given me by the goddess Durga. When I turn the pot upside down, a stream of cooked rice will come from the magic pot."

"My good husband," said the wife, "you have been so long in the forest. Are you sick and out of your mind?"

"Look! Look!" cried the Brahman. And he turned the pot upside down. But nothing came out of the old cooking pot.

The Second Magic Pot

The goddess Durga had given the poor Brahman a magic cooking pot. But the Innkeeper had put in its place one of his old cooking pots. When the Brahman got home, he wished to show his wife how cooked rice would come from the magic pot. He turned the pot upside down. But nothing came out of it.

The wife heard the Brahman's story and saw that nothing came from the cooking pot. She was sure that her husband was sick and was out of his mind.

The poor husband looked and looked at the old cooking pot. He did not know what had happened. Then he remembered that he had left the magic pot in the care of the Innkeeper.

The Innkeeper must have kept the magic pot and given him one of his own old cooking pots.

The poor Brahman hurried back to the inn.

"Innkeeper," said the Brahman, "give me the cooking pot that I left with you."

"I gave you your cooking pot," said the Innkeeper. He had his servants throw the Brahman out of the inn.

The Brahman then went into the forest where he had seen the goddess Durga. There the goddess Durga appeared to him.

"So you have lost the cooking pot that I gave to you," she said.

"I lost the magic pot because I left it with the Innkeeper," said the Brahman.

"I will give you another magic pot," said Durga. "But be sure that you make good use of it."

"Thank you, thank you," said the Brahman as he bowed to the ground. When he looked up, the goddess Durga was gone. But on the ground before him was a large cooking pot.

The Brahman picked up the pot and started home. But the pot was so big that he got tired and sat down to rest.

"I will see what this magic pot will do for me," said the Brahman to himself. He turned the pot upside down.

Out of the pot came a stream of demons. They carried sticks and they began to beat the Brahman.

The Brahman quickly turned the pot right side up. All the demons went back into the pot.

The Brahman sat on the ground and laughed and laughed.

"I know now why the goddess Durga said that I should make good use of this magic pot."

The Brahman hurried as fast as he could go to the inn. He set the big cooking pot by the door of the inn.

"Give me my cooking pot," cried the Brahman. But the Innkeeper came to the door and laughed at him.

Then the Brahman turned the pot upside down. A stream of demons came out of the pot. Each demon carried a stick.

The demons began to beat the Innkeeper and his servants.

"Stop. Stop," cried the Innkeeper. "Take your demons out of my inn."

"Give me my cooking pot," cried the Brahman.

"Yes. Yes," said the Innkeeper. "I will give you back your magic pot."

The Brahman turned the big pot right side up. And all the demons went back into the pot.

The Brahman took his two magic pots, that the goddess Durga had given him, to his home. He put the big pot away where the children could not find it. He did not want that pot turned upside down again.

But the Brahman turned the other pot upside down. A stream of cooked rice came out of the pot. The Brahman and his wife and his children were never hungry again.

The Donkey in the Lion's Skin

Once upon a time, there was a peddler who traveled from village to village. All of the peddler's pots were carried on the back of a donkey.

The peddler did not like to buy hay for his donkey. And so just before he came to a village, the peddler would tie a lion's skin over the donkey. Then he turned the donkey into a rice field.

The men who watched the rice fields saw what they thought was a lion eating the rice. They were very much afraid and did not go near the donkey in the lion's skin. And the donkey ate all the rice that he wanted.

The peddler would sell some pots in the village. In the evening, he would get his donkey out of the rice field and go on to the next village.

One day the peddler came to a rice field outside a village. He put the lion's skin on the donkey and turned the donkey into the rice field.

Two boys, who were brothers, were watching the rice field.

"Look," said one of the brothers. "I think I see a lion eating the rice that is in our father's rice field."

"We must go and tell our father," said the other brother.

The boys ran to the village. They told their father that a lion was eating the rice in the rice field. The father got the men and the boys of the village to come and help him drive the lion out of the rice field.

The men did not go near the lion, but they tried to frighten him. They made a great noise. The boys danced up and down and shouted and waved their arms.

The poor donkey became so frightened that he let out a loud cry.

"Listen to that cry," said the men of the village. "That cry is not the roar of a lion. That cry is the bray of a donkey."

The men rushed at the poor donkey and beat him. They beat him so hard that he died right there in the rice field.

The father of the two boys said, "My sons, you are good

watchers of my rice field. But if that poor donkey had only kept still, we would have thought he was a lion."

Now the peddler who would not buy hay for his donkey has to carry his pots on his back as he goes from village to village.

The Rabbits and the Elephant King

No rain had fallen for a long time. There was very little water in the rivers and in the lakes. The elephants could not find enough water to drink. There was no water for them to bathe in. The elephants were very much worried.

Then one of the young elephants spoke to the King of the herd of elephants.

"Oh, King, what are we to do? The little animals can find enough water in the little pools. But we eat grass all day and we need much water to drink. And we need water to bathe in."

The King of the elephants knew that he must find water for his herd. He must take them into new country.

So the King of the elephants led the herd off through the jungle. They went a long, long way. They were very tired. They needed water very much. Then suddenly, in the middle of the jungle, they came upon a large pool of water.

The elephants rushed into the

pool of water. They began to drink and drink the clear water. They filled their trunks with the water and threw it over their backs.

Now it so happened that many rabbits had made their homes in the banks beside the pool. As the elephants rushed into the water, their big feet destroyed the homes of many of the rabbits.

The King of the rabbits also lived beside the pool of water. He saw the homes of the rabbits being destroyed. He knew something must be done about it. So he began to think. At last he thought of what to do.

"I must talk to the King of the elephants," thought the King of the rabbits. "But the King of the elephants must not know that I am just a rabbit."

So the King of the rabbits went to a big rock that was covered by the jungle trees. He climbed up on top of the rock so that his voice would come from high up. Then he waited until the King of the elephants came by.

Then the King of the rabbits called out in a loud voice,

"Stop, King of the elephants.

Hear a messenger who is sent to you from the Moon god."

The King of the elephants stopped. He could not see anything.

"Who are you?" he said. "Where do you come from?"

"I am the messenger from the Moon god," said the rabbit. "The Moon god is very angry with you. At night, the Moon god bathes in the pool in the jungle. He has sent the rabbits to guard his pool. But last night the elephants frightened the rabbits away from the Moon god's pool."

"We did not know that it was

the pool of the Moon god," said the King of the elephants. "I hope that the Moon god is not angry."

"You must go alone into the pool tonight," said the rabbit. "You will find the Moon god in the pool. He is shaking with anger. Bow your head and ask him to forgive you. Promise him that the herd of elephants will never come to his pool again."

That night the King of the elephants went alone into the pool of water. He could see the Moon god in the water. For the moon was high in the sky and his reflection was in the water.

As the big elephant walked into the water, his feet made little waves in the water. The reflection of the Moon shook. The King of the elephants thought that he saw the Moon god shaking with anger. He bowed his head and said,

"Moon god, do not be angry. We will never drink or bathe in your pool again."

The herd of elephants went away. They never came again to the pool in the jungle.

The wise old rabbit and his friends made their homes in the banks around the pool. They lived there a long, long time.

The Black Ox

There was a Brahman who had a Black Ox. The Brahman loved this Black Ox and took care of him like a son. He gave him rice to eat and washed his black coat.

The Black Ox grew to be big and strong. The Black Ox grew to be the strongest Ox in all the land. One day the Black Ox said to himself,

"The Brahman has been very good to me. He has taken care of me like a son. I think that I should do something for him."

One day the Black Ox said to the Brahman,

"Go to the rich farmer and say to him, 'I bet a thousand pieces of money that my ox will pull a hundred carts filled with stone!' "

The Brahman went to the rich farmer and he said,

"Do you know anyone who has a very strong ox?"

"There are no stronger oxen in the country than my fine oxen," said the rich farmer.

"Do you have an ox that could pull a hundred carts filled with stones?" asked the Brahman.

The farmer laughed and laughed.

"There is no ox in the world that could pull a hundred carts filled with stones," he said.

"I have a Black Ox," said the Brahman. "He can pull a hundred carts filled with stones."

"Will you make a bet with me?" asked the rich farmer.

"Yes," said the Brahman. "I bet a thousand pieces of money that my Black Ox can pull a hundred carts filled with stones."

So the bet was made.

The Brahman went home and got his Black Ox. The rich farmer got a hundred carts and filled them with stones.

The Brahman tied one cart behind the other. He hitched the Black Ox to the front cart.

Then the Brahman waved his whip and cried in an angry voice,

"Get up, you lazy ox. Pull. Pull those carts, you lazy ox."

The Black Ox said to himself,

"The Brahman has never talked that way to me before. He called me lazy."

The Black Ox stood still. He would not try to pull.

The rich farmer laughed and laughed.

"Pay me the thousand pieces of money, Brahman. Your Black Ox will not even try to pull the hundred carts filled with stones."

The Brahman paid the rich farmer a thousand pieces of money. And he took his Black Ox home.

That night the Black Ox said to the Brahman,

"Are you asleep?"

"No," said the Brahman. "I cannot sleep. I had to pay the rich farmer a thousand pieces of money."

"I have always been a good ox," said the Black Ox.

"Yes," said the Brahman. "You have always been a good ox. But why did you not try to pull the hundred carts filled with stones?"

"You have always been good to me," said the Black Ox. "But why did you call me lazy? That is why I did not try to pull the carts."

"I am sorry that I called you lazy," said the Brahman. "I only called to you as I know the rich farmer calls to his oxen."

"Go again to the rich farmer," said the Black Ox. "Bet him two thousand pieces of money that your ox can pull a hundred carts filled with stones."

The Brahman went to the rich farmer and the bet was made. The hundred carts were filled with stones and tied together. The Black Ox was hitched to the front cart.

This time the Brahman used no whip. He just called to his Black Ox.

"Pull, my beautiful Black Ox. Pull. Pull, my beautiful, strong Black Ox."

And the Black Ox pulled the hundred carts filled with stone.

The rich farmer saw that the Brahman had won the bet. He gave the Brahman two thousand pieces of money. And that was enough money for the Brahman and the Black Ox to buy everything that they wanted.

The What-Fruit Tree

Once upon a time, there was a rich, rich Merchant. He went from city to city to sell his goods. He had five hundred wagons that carried the beautiful things that he had to sell.

This rich Merchant had many servants and helpers. He was good and kind. He tried to look after the people who worked for him.

One day the wagons of the Merchant came to a forest. He stopped them and spoke to all his servants and helpers.

"It has been told to me that

many poisonous trees grow in this forest. Many men die here in the forest. So I want all my servants and helpers to promise that they will not eat a leaf, a flower, or a fruit in this forest until they have asked me about it."

Then the wagons and the people went on.

In the middle of the forest they came near a village. Just outside the village grew a tree full of fruit.

Under this fruit tree, the people with the wagons stopped to rest. The way through the forest had been long and hard.

"Look," said one of the helpers. "Here is a mango tree and it is filled with fruit. Let us eat, for we are tired and hungry."

"No! No!" said one of the servants. "Our Master had told us to eat nothing until we have asked him about it."

Just then the Merchant came up to the tree. One of the servants showed him the fruit.

"This is a what-fruit tree," said the Merchant. "It is very poisonous. If you were to eat of the fruit, you would surely die. And many men do eat the fruit, for they think it is a mango."

"Let us sleep this night under the what-fruit tree," he said. "In the morning the men of the village will come out to us."

It happened just as the Merchant had said. In the morning the men of the village came out to the what-fruit tree. And they all looked very much astonished.

One of the servants of the Merchant heard what the villagers were saying.

"This has never happened before," they said to one another. "Always in the morning we found dead men under the what-fruit tree. Always we have taken the things from the wagons and kept them for ourselves."

Then one of the villagers went up to the servant.

"How did you know that this is not a mango tree?" he asked.

"We did not know," said the servant. "But our Master knew. He is a good and wise man."

The villagers talked among themselves, and then they went up to the Merchant.

"Tell us, good and wise man," they said, "how you knew that this was not a mango tree?"

The Merchant looked at the

villagers and he did not look with kindness.

"Two things told me that this was not a mango tree," he said. "First, this tree grew just outside a village. It could easily be reached by all the people. Second, the tree could easily be climbed, and the fruit eaten. But none was eaten. That could mean only one thing. The fruit was poisonous. Then I remembered that I had heard of the tree that looks like a mango but is not."

Then the Merchant, the good and wise man, spoke angrily to the villagers.

"But you yourselves are evil men. You wished my servants to die so that you could rob them of all our goods. You would have killed us with the poison fruit. But you shall not do that again."

So the Merchant ordered his servants to take their axes and to cut down the what-fruit tree. They went to work. Soon it was upon the ground, a dead tree that would kill no one any more.

Then the Merchant and his men went on and had nothing whatever to do with the village and its people.

LAITE

The Smart Monkey

Every evening the monkeys came down to the river with their Chief. First they took a drink of water from the river. Then they ran to the mango tree that stood alone beside the river.

When the monkeys had eaten all the mangoes that they could hold, the Chief led the monkeys home to the trees of the forest nearby. The monkeys had a very happy life.

Far down the river from where the mango tree grew, a fisherman was fishing in the river. In the water, he found a fruit he had never seen before. He took this strange fruit to the King.

"Is this fruit good to eat?" asked the King.

"I do not know," said the fisherman.

"This fruit must grow upon a tree," said the King. "Call my foresters. They know all the trees in the forest."

When the foresters came, they looked at the strange fruit.

"This fruit is called a mango," said one of the foresters. "It grows upon a mango tree. It must have come from many miles up the river. There a beautiful mango tree grows beside the river."

"Is the fruit good to eat?" asked the King.

"Yes," said the foresters. "The mango is very good to eat."

The fruit was cut open and the King ate some of the mango. He liked it so much that he wanted more.

The King said to the foresters, "Take me to the mango tree that grows beside the river."

The King and the princes and the soldiers and the servants made ready for the journey up the river. They got many boats ready.

Then the servants pushed the boats up the river with poles. The King sat on a golden chair and watched the monkeys in the tree tops. It was a beautiful journey.

At last the forester called out,

"Oh, King, here is the mango tree beside the river. And on the ground under the tree you will find many mangoes."

The servants tied the boats to the bank of the river. The King and the princes and the soldiers went under the mango tree. They ate the mangoes. Everyone thought that the mangoes were very good.

The sun was going down. It was getting dark.

"We must sleep under the mango tree," said the King. "In the morning we will pick the mangoes from the tree and take them with us."

The King and the princes and the soldiers and the servants were fast asleep when the monkeys came to the mango tree. They started to eat the mangoes. They made so much noise that the soldiers woke up.

"We must shoot those monkeys with our bows and arrows in the morning when we can see them," said the soldiers.

In the morning, the monkeys heard the soldiers getting ready to shoot them. They were very much afraid. They said to their Chief,

"What shall we do? The soldiers are all ready to shoot us. We cannot get away from this tree because it stands alone by the river."

"Do not be afraid," said the Chief of the monkeys. "I will see that you all get away from here."

The Chief of the monkeys had seen that there were trees across the river. He went out along the branch of the mango tree that went out over the river. It came near to a branch of a tree from across the river. The Chief of the monkeys said to himself,

"I could jump from this branch to that branch of the tree across the river. But the little monkeys could not jump that far."

The Chief of the monkeys thought for a time. Then he said to himself,

"I know what I will do. I will make a bridge of my back for the little monkeys."

The Chief of the monkeys took hold of the branch of the mango tree with his long tail. Then he jumped to the branch of the tree that grew across the river. He held on to the mango branch with his tail and he held on to the other branch with his hands. He called to the other monkeys,

"Come out on the long branch of the mango tree. Then walk carefully over my back to the branch of the other tree."

The sun was just coming up. The King woke up and looked up into the mango tree. He saw the monkeys going from the mango tree to the tree across the river, along the back of the big monkey.

"Do not shoot the monkeys," cried the King. "The Chief of the monkey people is a smart monkey. He is willing to do all he can for his people. And I promise that he and his people will have the mangoes from this tree as long as they wish."

And that is why no one ever picks the mangoes from the tree that grows along by the river. The mangoes on the tree must be left for the Chief of the monkeys and his people.

LAITE

The Man Who Lost His Cow

Once upon a time there was a Rajah who was very rich. But he was not a kind man. He took whatever he could get. And no one living in his country would say no to anything that the Rajah said.

The Rajah had a herd of cows. He told his herd-boy that whenever a strange cow got into this herd, the herd-boy was to keep it. The Rajah had more cows than anyone in his kingdom.

There lived near the Rajah a man who had only one cow. One day he could not find his cow. All day long the man hunted for his cow. And the next day he found his cow in the Rajah's herd of cows. But the herd-boy would not let the man have his cow without an order from the Rajah.

The man went to the Rajah. He told the Rajah how his cow had run away and had got into the herd of the Rajah's cows. He asked the Rajah to give him an order to the herd-boy so that the herd-boy would let him take his cow home. But the Rajah would not listen to the man. He had his servants put the man out of the palace.

Then the man went to his friends and told them how he had lost his cow. He told them that the Rajah would not give his cow back to him. But the friends said,

"We can do nothing for you. The Rajah takes what he wants. You have lost your cow."

The unhappy man went and sat by the river. He talked to himself and said,

"The Rajah has many cows.

And I had only one cow. It is not right that the Rajah should keep my cow. But no one will help me get my cow back."

A Jackal was sitting by the bank of the river. He heard what the man said to himself. He was sorry for the man. So he spoke to him.

"If you will do just what I say," said the Jackal, "I am sure you can get your cow back. Go to the Rajah and say that you want the matter of the cow put before a council of the village. The law gives you the right to do this. But the council is not to meet in the Rajah's palace. It is to meet in an open field by the river."

The man went back to the Rajah and told him that by the laws of the country he wanted a council of the village to settle the matter of the cow.

The Rajah knew the law, and so he called a council. The man said,

"I want the council to meet in the field beside the river and I will show them how my cow was lost."

The council of the village and all the people of the village met in the field beside the river.

"Tell your story to the council," said the Rajah. And the Rajah was very angry, for no one had ever questioned him before.

The man stood up before the council. He told them about how his cow had been lost, and how it had got into the herd of the Rajah. No one noticed that a Jackal lay under a tree as if he were asleep.

The Rajah then told the council to settle the matter of the cow.

But not a man would speak, for they were all afraid of the Rajah.

The Rajah turned to the man and said,

"Where are the people who are going to settle the matter of the cow?"

The man pointed to the Jackal who lay under the tree.

"He will be my judge," said the man.

"It is a poor judge that goes to sleep," said the Rajah.

Then the Jackal opened his eyes and said,

"I have just had a wonderful

dream. Oh, great Rajah, I am sure that you can tell what my dream means."

Now the Rajah thought that he could tell the meanings of dreams. So he said to the Jackal,

"Tell us your dream."

"Well," said the Jackal, "I will tell you my dream. But if you cannot tell me what the dream means, you must give this man's cow back to him."

The Rajah wanted to hear about the dream. And he was sure that he could tell the meaning of dreams.

"Yes, yes," said the Rajah. "If

I cannot tell the meaning of your dream, I will give the man his cow."

Then the people of the village all said to the jackal,

"Now tell us your dream."

LAITE

The Jackal's Dream

The people of the village and the Rajah listened to the Jackal's dream.

The Jackal sat very still, with his eyes closed. Then he opened his eyes and said,

"I saw three die in one place. One died because he was sleepy. One died because he was angry. And one died because he was hungry. They all died in one place."

The people of the village all said,

"Oh, great Rajah, tell us the meaning of the strange dream."

But the Rajah could not tell the meaning of this strange dream. He was very angry, and he called out,

"This is just a Jackal's dream. There is no meaning to it. And who but a Jackal would go to sleep at a council."

"I did not go to sleep at a council meeting," said the Jackal. "The great god Thakur sent me here to help the man who had lost his cow. Now if you cannot tell why three died in one place, you must give the man back his cow."

The people of the village shouted, "Oh, Rajah, tell us why three died in one place?"

The Rajah began to be afraid. He could not think how three could die in one place. And he knew now that the great god Thakur had sent the Jackal to trick him.

At last he asked the Jackal to tell him how three could die in one place.

But the Jackal said, "First, great Rajah, you must put in

writing that you will give the man his cow."

The Rajah put in writing that he would give the man his cow. Then the Jackal told his story.

Once upon a time, an elephant was coming home through the forest. All day long the elephant had been eating the green leaves from the trees. Now the elephant was tired and sleepy. He lay down and went to sleep.

It so happened that the elephant lay down right on the home of a snake. The snake could not get out of his hole. And the snake became very angry. The snake bit the elephant while he was sleeping and the elephant died.

The snake could not get out of the hole. It could not get any air or any food. And so the snake died.

A jackal came through the forest. The jackal was very hungry. When he saw the dead elephant, he made a hole in the skin of the elephant and began to eat the meat. The jackal was so hungry that he ate and he ate. Pretty soon he was inside the elephant.

The sun was very hot, and it

made the skin of the elephant dry and hard. The skin closed the hole that the jackal had made in the elephant. The jackal could not get out. And so the jackal died inside the elephant.

Now the Jackal who was telling the story smiled at all the people of the village. He smiled at the Rajah. And he said,

"Oh, great Rajah, that is the meaning of the three that died in one place. The elephant died because he was sleepy. The snake died because it was angry. And the jackal died because he was hungry."

The Rajah gave the man back his cow. All the people of the village were glad for him.

The Jackal went away, and he was never seen again.

LAITE

Wealth or Wisdom

Once upon a time, there was a Rajah and a Merchant who each had a fine son. The boys were great friends. They played together. They went to school together. And they were always arguing about one thing.

The young Prince would say,

"I think that wealth can get me anything in the world."

"No! No!" said the Merchant's son. "It is wisdom that can get you what you want in this world."

Day after day the boys argued.

The boys grew to be fine young men. And still they argued.

At last the Merchant's son said,

"Let us find out if it is wealth or wisdom that can get us what we want in this world. Let us go to a strange country where no one knows who we are. Let us stay there for one year and find out if it is wealth or wisdom that gets us what we want."

One morning, the two young men went off to a strange country. And no one knew where they had gone.

Now the Prince, the son of the Rajah, had with him all the money that he wanted. He went to a big city and bought a fine house and had parties for a lot of people.

But the Merchant's son had to find work so that he could have a place to sleep and enough to eat. He went to a village and began to teach school. The children of the school loved their teacher and he had a very happy life.

One day the Prince came to the Merchant's son.

"My good friend," said the Prince, "I have spent all of my money. I have no place to sleep and nothing to eat. I must get some work to do or I will have to go back to my father's palace. And I have promised not to go back before a year is up."

A farmer who lived in the village wanted a servant to look after his ox. The Merchant's son went to the farmer and said,

"I have a friend who will look after your ox."

The Prince became a servant and worked for the farmer. He did not want to go back to his father's palace before the year was up.

But the farmer was not a very good man. He did not want to

pay his servants what he should. He said to his new servant,

"I will give you each day all the cooked rice that I can put on a green leaf. But I will give you no money until I see how you can work."

The Prince had never been a servant before. And so he thought that what the farmer said was all right.

He went to work for the farmer.

Every morning the Prince took the farmer's ox out to the field. But the field had no fence around it. The ox would run away from the field again and again. The

Prince had a hard time getting the ox back into the field.

In the evening, the Prince brought the ox back to his shed. There the Prince had to fill the water trough so that the ox could drink. But the water trough had holes in the bottom. The water would run out.

When evening came, the farmer said that he was not pleased with his servant's work. He gave him his cooked rice on the smallest leaf that he could find. It was only a mouthful of rice.

Day after day the same thing happened. The poor Prince was

always hungry. And he did not know what to do.

One day the Merchant's son came to see how his friend was getting along. When he saw how sick the Prince looked and heard the story of the ox, he said,

"I will take your place as servant to the farmer. You go to the village and teach my school."

The next morning, when the Merchant's son took the ox out to the field, he took a long rope with him. He tied the ox to a tree. And the ox did not run away that day.

In the evening, when the

Merchant's son came to fill the trough for the ox, he saw the holes in the bottom. So he put mud in the bottom of the trough to stop the holes. And the water did not run out.

In the evening, when the Merchant's son went to the farmer for his rice, he brought the largest leaf he could find. The farmer had to fill the leaf with cooked rice, as he had promised.

As the leaf was almost three feet long, the farmer's wife said,

"It will take my whole pot of rice to fill that leaf."

"It is only one leaf," said the Merchant's son.

When the year was up, the farmer was only too glad to have his servant leave. For no matter what he asked the servant to do, the servant had the wisdom to get the better of him.

Then the Merchant's son and the Rajah's son went back to their own country.

"It has been a wonderful year," said the Rajah's son to his friend. "From now on, we will not argue. Wealth is something that you may not keep. But wisdom is something that you can keep all your life."

The Green Parrot

There was a hunter who caught birds in the forest. Then he took the birds to the city to sell.

One day his wife said to him,

"My good husband, I am hungry. Today let us eat the birds that you catch in the forest."

The hunter and his wife went into the forest. But they did not catch any birds. As the sun was going down, the hunter caught a beautiful green parrot. He gave it to his wife.

"This bird will make only a mouthful of food," said the hunter.

"It is such a pretty bird," said the wife.

"Do not kill me," said the Green Parrot.

The hunter and his wife were very much surprised.

"I never before heard a bird talk," said the wife. "What do you want me to do with you, Green Parrot?"

"Take me to the King," said the Green Parrot. "He will buy me. I will speak to him and name my own price."

The next morning the hunter took the Green Parrot to the King.

The King thought that the Green Parrot was the most beautiful bird that he had ever seen. He wanted to buy it.

"How much do you want for the bird?" asked the King.

"Great King," said the hunter, "the Green Parrot will name his own price."

The King laughed.

"Can a parrot talk?" he asked. Then he turned to the Green Parrot and said,

"What is the price of a Green Parrot?"

"Great King," said the Green Parrot, "my price is ten thousand rupees. And do not think that ten thousand rupees is a high price, for I can be of great help to you."

"How can a parrot help a King?" the King asked.

"When your need is great, you will find that I can save your life," said the Green Parrot.

The King was surprised to hear a parrot talk. He was surprised to hear that a parrot could save his life. So he gave the hunter ten thousand rupees.

The hunter went home to his

wife and they never again wanted for anything.

The King spent all of his time with the Green Parrot. Any question he asked, the Green Parrot answered. And the answers were both wise and good. The Green Parrot told the King the names of all the Hindu gods. By naming the names, the King grew in favor with the gods.

The King had six Queens, but the King spent all of his time talking with the Green Parrot. The six Queens were very angry with the Green Parrot. They planned to kill it so that the King would again pay attention to them.

One day the King went hunting. He went into the forest and was gone two days.

"Now we can kill the Green Parrot," said the First Queen.

"Who will kill it?" asked the Second Queen.

"We will ask the Green Parrot which of us is the ugliest," said the First Queen.

"Then the one of us that the Parrot says is the ugliest will have to kill the bird," said the Third Queen.

The six Queens all thought that a very good plan. They went to the room in the palace where the Green Parrot lived in a golden cage.

But before any one of the Queens could ask, "Which one of us is the ugliest Queen?" the Green Parrot began to tell them the names of all the Hindu gods.

The six Queens went back to their rooms in the palace.

"We cannot kill such a holy bird," said the Fourth Queen.

But the next day the Fifth Queen said,

"We must kill the Green Parrot today or it will be too late. The King will come back tonight."

The six Queens went to the room in the palace where the Green Parrot lived in a golden cage.

"Green Parrot," said the Sixth Queen, "tell us which Queen is the prettiest, and which Queen is the ugliest."

The Green Parrot knew that the wicked Queens had come to kill him. So he said to them,

"If I am to answer your questions, I must first look at

each one of you very carefully. And if I am to see you very well, you must let me out of this cage."

At first the six Queens did not want to let the Green Parrot out of the golden cage. But at last they shut all the doors and the windows in the room. And then they let the bird out of his cage.

The Green Parrot flew about the room. He saw a hole at the top of one of the windows. Then he flew down and sat on the back of a chair.

"Now that I have stretched my wings," said the Green Parrot, "I will try to answer your questions. Will each Queen stand before me so that I can look closely at her beauty."

Each Queen stood before the bird and he looked at her with his bright eyes. But not a word did he say.

At last, very thoughtfully, he began to speak as if he were talking to himself.

"I see six beautiful women before me. But not one of them is as beautiful as the Princess who lives beyond the Seven Seas."

The six Queens were very angry. They all rushed at the Green

Parrot and wished to kill him. But the Green Parrot flew up so that the Queens could not catch him.

The Green Parrot flew out of the hole at the top of the window. He flew to the hut of a woodcutter. The woodcutter and his wife took care of the Green Parrot.

The Most Beautiful Princess in the World

When the King came back from his hunting, the Green Parrot was gone. The King was heartbroken.

The servants looked in every part of the palace. But they could not find the Green Parrot.

The King asked his six Queens if any of them had seen the Green Parrot. But each one of the Queens said that she knew nothing about the Green Parrot.

Then the King sent messengers to every part of his kingdom. He said he would give ten thousand rupees to anyone who would bring back the Green Parrot.

Many people came and brought green parrots to the King. But not one of the parrots could talk.

One day, the Green Parrot, who was living in the forest with the woodcutter, said to the man,

"My friend, I want you to take me to the King. He will give you ten thousand rupees for me."

The woodcutter was so surprised to hear a bird talk that he took the Green Parrot to the King at once.

The King was sitting on his throne. He was very sick. And he was very tired, for he had looked at hundreds of green birds.

"I shall never see my Green Parrot again," said the King. And he did not look very closely at the green bird that the woodcutter brought.

"Great and good King," said the Green Parrot, "I am home again. Give my friend, the woodcutter, the ten thousand rupees, for he has taken good care of me."

The King and all of the people in the palace were happy. That is, all except the six Queens.

"Why did you fly away from my palace, O beautiful Green Parrot?" asked the King.

"I told your six Queens that I knew where the most beautiful Princess in the world lived. And your six Queens were going to kill me," said the Green Parrot.

The King was so angry with the six Queens that he sent them to live in a house by themselves.

Then the King said to the Green Parrot,

"Take me to the most beautiful Princess in the world."

"We must have a magic horse," said the Green Parrot. "The

Princess lives in a castle which is over the Thirteen Rivers and the Seven Seas."

"But where can I find a magic horse?" asked the King.

"Let us look at all your horses," said the Green Parrot. "One of them may be a magic horse."

The Green Parrot and the King looked at all the beautiful horses. But the wise parrot said that no one of them was a magic horse. Then the Green Parrot went out and looked at every horse in the kingdom. At last he found a poor, ugly pony.

"This pony will grow to be a

magic horse," said the Green Parrot. "He must have a stable all to himself. And he must be fed on the finest of grain."

Everything was done just as the Green Parrot said. In six months, the horse was ready for the journey across the Thirteen Rivers and the Seven Seas.

"Before we start," said the Green Parrot, "we must have a bag of silver rice."

The King did just what the Green Parrot told him to do. So he had a bag of silver rice made. This was silver made in exactly the shape of grains of rice.

At last the King and the Green Parrot were ready to start. They got upon the magic horse.

"Listen to what I tell you," said the Green Parrot. "When you whip this horse, whip him only once. Never whip him twice."

The King whipped the magic horse once. Away they went up in the air like the wind. When the sun was going down, the horse set them down at the gate of a beautiful castle.

Beside the gate of the castle grew a big tree. The Green Parrot told the King to hide in the tree. Then the Green Parrot said that he would bring the Princess to the King.

Then the Green Parrot took the bag of silver rice. He started at the tree. He dropped a grain of rice every foot of the way. He went through the gate of the castle. He went through the castle. He went right to the door of the bedroom of the Princess. Every foot of the way, the Green Parrot dropped a grain of silver rice.

In the morning, when the Princess came out of her bedroom, she saw the silver rice. She got a basket and began to pick up the pretty bits of silver. At last she came to the tree that grew beside the gate of the castle. Then the King jumped down from the tree and said,

"Most beautiful Princess in the World, I have come to ask you to be my wife."

The Princess smiled and said yes.

The King and the Princess got on the magic horse. The Green Parrot sat upon the King's shoulder. The King whipped the horse just once. Up they went into the air like the wind.

The Magic Horse

The King and the beautiful Princess and the Green Parrot were flying on the magic horse back to his kingdom.

But the King was in a hurry to get back to his kingdom. He forgot what the Green Parrot had told him. He whipped the magic horse twice.

Down the horse went to the earth. He could no longer fly through the air.

"Oh, what have you done?" cried the Green Parrot. "You did

not remember what I told you. You whipped the magic horse twice."

The King and the Princess and the Green Parrot and the magic horse were left in a forest in a strange country.

One day the king of that country was hunting in the forest. He saw the beautiful Princess and wanted her for his wife. He called his soldiers and they took the Princess away from the King who had found her in the far country.

The King fought with the soldiers, but he was just one man against many. He was not killed, but his eyes were hurt so that he could no longer see. So the soldiers took away his Princess and the magic horse. They left the blind King in the forest. But they did not see a Green Parrot that was up in a tree.

"Great King," said the Green Parrot, "I will take care of you so that you will not die in the forest."

Every day the Green Parrot brought fruit from the trees for the King to eat. And so they lived in the forest.

The king of the country took the Beautiful Princess back to his palace, and wished to marry her.

But the beautiful Princess told the king that she could not marry him for six months. She had made a promise to the gods that she would pray and feed the birds for six months.

The Princess also told the king that she must have a stable and the finest of grain for her horse. The king gave the Princess everything that she asked for. He thought she was the most beautiful Princess in the world.

Every day the Princess fed the birds, for she was sure that one day the Green Parrot would come to her and tell her what had happened to the man she loved. Every day she fed the magic horse with the best of grain, for she was sure that some day the magic horse could fly again.

In the forest, the Green Parrot worked hard to find fruit for the blind King. One day the birds of the forest said to the Green Parrot,

"You have a hard life in the forest. Come with us to the palace where a lady feeds us grain every day."

So the Green Parrot went to the palace where the Princess was feeding the birds.

The Green Parrot ate the grain

out of the hand of the Princess. He said to her so that no one could hear him,

"Most beautiful Princess, the King that you love still lives in the forest. But he is blind and cannot find his way here. I am looking after him."

"Dear Green Parrot," said the Princess, "thank you for looking after my King."

Then she told the Green Parrot that she had been feeding the magic horse and that now he was almost ready to fly again.

"But first we must cure the King's blindness," said the Princess.

"There is a blue egg that is in a nest in the tree that grows beside the gate of my father's castle. Go and get this blue egg. Break it on the eyes of my King. Then he will be cured of his blindness."

The Green Parrot flew back to the forest. He told the blind King all that the Princess had said. He fed the King some fruit. Then he said,

"Great King, sleep and rest. I am going to get the blue egg that will cure your blindness."

The Green Parrot flew over the Thirteen Rivers and the Seven Seas. He found the blue egg that was in the nest in the tree that grew beside the gate of the castle. He put the blue egg in a little bag. He tied the bag around his neck. Then the Green Parrot flew back over the Thirteen Rivers and the Seven Seas.

The Green Parrot was very tired. But he flew right to the blind King in the forest. He broke the blue egg upon the King's eyes. And the King could see again.

After the Green Parrot had rested, he flew to the palace. As he ate the grain from the hand of the Princess, he said,

"All is ready. Come to the forest with the magic horse."

The next day, the Princess came to the forest with the magic horse. The King, the Princess, and the Green Parrot got on the horse. Up in the air they went like the wind. And this time the King remembered. He whipped the magic horse only once.

That is the story of the most beautiful Princess in the world and the King that she loved and the Green Parrot that loved them both.

The Hate of Sani

Sani was the god of bad luck. And Lakshmi was the goddess of good luck.

"I am more powerful than you are," said Sani to Lakshmi. "Bad luck will destroy any man on earth."

"No! No!" said Lakshmi, "I am more powerful than you are, for good luck is stronger than bad."

"Let us find some good and wise man on earth," said Sani. "We will try our powers on him."

Now there was a rich man on earth whose name was Sribatsa.

He was both good and wise. Sani and Lakshmi sent a messenger to tell Sribatsa that they would come to visit him to ask him which was the most powerful.

Sribatsa did not know what to do. If he said that Sani was the most powerful, Lakshmi would take his good luck away. But if he said that Lakshmi was the most powerful, Sani would hate him and bad luck would follow him wherever he went.

Sribatsa had two chairs made for his visitors. One chair was made of gold and one chair was made of silver. And when his visitors came, Sribatsa asked Sani to sit in the silver chair.

Sani was very angry.

"You ask me to sit in a silver chair. But you left the golden chair for Lakshmi to sit upon. Am I less powerful than Lakshmi? I shall show you. For three years my hate shall be upon you."

Then Lakshmi spoke.

"Be not afraid," she said. "I will always be your friend."

Then the god and the goddess went back to the heavens.

Sribatsa spoke to his wife.

"My dear Chintamani," he said, "I must leave you and our house or the hate of Sani will come upon it and upon you."

"Where you go, I will go," said Chintamani.

Sribatsa took a large bag. In it he put his gold. He also put in the bag all of Chintamani's jewels. Then he put the bag on his head. And he and his wife set out upon their journey.

Sribatsa and Chintamani soon came to a river. They asked a man with a small boat to take them over the river.

"You are three," said the man, "a man and a woman and a large and heavy bag. I can only take one at a time in my little boat. I will take the bag first."

The man put the bag into the little boat and got in. He started across the river. But a great wind suddenly turned the boat upside down. The man and the bag were lost in the river.

"It is the hate of Sani," said Sribatsa. Then he and his wife walked along the banks of the river until they came to a village.

Sribatsa had no money and so he helped the weavers, who made beautiful cloth. Chintamani made good things for the weavers to eat.

Then the weavers said to their wives,

"Why don't you cook like Chintamani?" And the wives hated Chintamani.

One day Chintamani and the other women of the village went to the river to bathe. By the bank there was a fishing boat.

The fishermen carried Chintamani off in their boat. None of the women of the village tried to help her.

When the women of the village told Sribatsa that the fishermen had carried his wife off in their boat, he cried,

"The hate of Sani has fallen on Chintamani, too."

Sribatsa rushed to the river, but the boat was nowhere to be seen.

All day long, Sribatsa went along the river. Sometimes he thought that he saw the boat far away. At other times, he could see no boat upon the river.

When night came, Sribatsa found himself in a garden of flowers that was by the river. He was so tired that he lay under a tree and slept.

Now the garden belonged to an old woman. Every day the old woman took flowers to the palace of the King. When she went to cut her flowers that morning, she found Sribatsa asleep in her garden. She woke him and took him to her hut and gave him food and drink.

"Where have you come from?" asked the old woman.

"I have come a long way," said Sribatsa. "And I am looking for my wife who has been stolen by some fishermen."

"Perhaps the King can help you," said the old woman. "Come with me when I take my flowers to the palace of the King."

The King saw that Sribatsa was a wise man and a good man.

"What work do you wish to do?" asked the King.

"I wish to guard the gates of the river," said Sribatsa.

Sribatsa thought that if he saw every boat on the river, he would be sure at some time to find the boat of the fishermen who had stolen Chintamani.

So Sribatsa was made the one to guard the river. He stopped every boat and made sure no stolen things were on the boat.

One day the fishermen who had stolen Chintamani came down the river. Sribatsa had his soldiers stop the boat.

The soldiers found Chintamani on the boat unharmed, for the goddess Lakshmi had protected her. They also found much gold and jewels that the fishermen had stolen.

Sribatsa and the soldiers took the gold and the jewels to the King. And when he was before the King, Sribatsa told him the story of the Hate of Sani.

"Now the three years are up," said Sribatsa. "The goddess of good luck has won. Lakshmi has brought my beautiful wife, Chintamani, back to me unharmed."

The King was glad to hear the story. He had a great festival in honor of Sribatsa and Chintamani. Then he sent them back to their own country with much gold.

Young Rama

It was evening. The baby Rama saw the big yellow moon. He reached out his arms, but he could not touch the moon. The baby Rama cried and cried.

Rama's mother took the baby in her arms and rocked him. She showed him her beautiful jewels that shone in the moonlight. But the baby still cried and cried and reached out his arms for the moon.

At last the mother sent for the baby's father, who was the Maharajah Dasaratha.

"My lord," she said, "Rama cries and cries. I do not know what to do. But if he does not stop crying he will get sick and die.

Dasaratha did not know what to do. Rama was his favorite son. He was to rule as the Maharajah when Dasaratha died. And so he sent for his Chief Counsellor.

The Chief Counsellor came and sat beside the baby. The baby, Rama, cried and cried. And he reached out his arms toward the moon.

"Ah," said the Chief Counsellor, "our baby Rama wants the moon.

And the gods have said that what Rama wants, he will always get."

"What are we to do?" cried Dasaratha. "I cannot get my son the moon. And if he does not stop crying, he will surely die."

Then the Chief Counsellor put a mirror into the hands of the baby Rama. In the mirror, the baby saw the reflection of the moon. He thought he had the moon in his hands. He stopped crying, and he laughed and laughed.

Dasaratha said, "Chief Counsellor, you have saved the life of the next Maharajah."

Now Rama was the son of the

Maharajah's first wife. The Maharajah had three wives, for that was the custom in India in those days. And each wife had a son, so there were three sons.

The three boys grew up together in the Maharajah's palace. They loved one another as brothers. They went to the palace school together. They learned to shoot bows and arrows too. They learned to ride elephants and to drive chariots.

Rama was the biggest and the strongest of the three boys. He could run the fastest. He could shoot an arrow and always hit what he shot at. He was not afraid of wild elephants or of wild horses. And the other boys were always glad that Rama could do these things.

One day, a Holy Man came to the palace. The Maharajah welcomed the Holy Man.

"Most holy of men," said Dasaratha, the Maharajah, "tell me something that I can do for you."

"I have come to you, great ruler and great warrior," said the Holy Man. "For the Rakshasa, or giant evil ones, have sent demons to harm me. They eat the sacrifices that I place upon the altars. I ask that you send your son Rama to drive them away."

"But Rama is only a boy of sixteen," said Dasaratha. "He could not win a fight against the Rakshasa. Take a hundred of my soldiers to help you. But do not ask that Rama go. He must be the Maharajah when I am dead."

"It is only Rama that I need to help me," said the Holy Man. "Rama is protected by the gods. He only can win a fight against the Rakshasa and drive the demons away from my altar."

At last the Maharajah said that

Rama could go to the temple in the mountains where the Holy Man had his altar.

"I want my son Lakshmana to go with Rama," said Dasaratha. "He will take care of Rama."

The next day the Holy Man and Prince Lakshmana and Prince Rama went toward the mountains. They came to the deep jungle at the foot of the mountains where a wicked Rakshasa woman lived. She threw great stones on the two Princes and tried to kill them.

Rama put two arrows to his bow at one time and shot them into both the arms of the wicked

Rakshasa woman. Then she, by her magic, changed her shape and became invisible. But she still made a rain of stones to fall upon the two Princes.

Then Rama listened. He could not see the Rakshasa woman but he heard her moving like a wind. He shot a great arrow and killed the wicked Rakshasa.

The Holy Man kissed Rama upon the head.

"Surely you are a son of the gods and they will always protect you," he said.

Then the Holy Man prayed a powerful prayer. As he prayed,

out of the heavens came magic weapons for Rama. The spirit of each weapon stood before Rama and said,

"We are your servants."

"When I have need of you, I will call you," Rama said to the spirits.

The Holy Man and Lakshmana and Rama went up the mountain to the temple. Rama, with the help of the magic weapons, killed the demons who were eating the sacrifice from the altar of the gods.

Rama and Sita

The next morning, the Holy Man said to Rama and Lakshmana,

"I must go to the country of Mithila. I want you to go with me."

Rama and Lakshmana went with the Holy Man to the country of Mithila. And as they journeyed, the Holy Man told the princes the story of the Great Bow of Shiva that King Janaka guarded.

"Janaka, the Rajah, has a most beautiful daughter," said the Holy Man. "He has promised her in marriage to the man who can bend the Great Bow of Shiva."

When the Holy Man and the two Princes reached Mithila, they were welcomed with great honor by Janaka, the Rajah. There was much feasting.

Then, at one of the great feasts, Janaka gave orders that the Great Bow of Shiva be brought out. It came in a golden chariot drawn by ten oxen. It was the greatest bow that Rama had ever seen.

But Rama stepped up to the chariot and picked up the bow. There was a great shout, for few men could even lift the bow.

Then Rama held the bow in one hand and the string in the other. He pulled the string and the bow bent. He pulled and pulled, and the bow bent and bent. Then the great bow snapped in two with the sound of thunder.

The people fell on their faces and cried, "The god Shiva has spoken in the thunder."

Janaka spoke to Rama.

"When my daughter Sita was born, I promised that I would give her in marriage to the man who could bend the bow of Shiva. You, Rama, are the one that the gods have smiled upon. You are the one to whom the gods have given their strength.

"I now give my daughter, the most beautiful Princess in the world, to be your wife. You will send for your father, Dasaratha, and his Queens. The marriage will take place as soon as they can get here."

Rama looked at Sita and he thought that surely she was the most beautiful woman in the world.

All the rest of their lives, Rama and Sita loved each other. And the story of their love for each other is one of the beautiful stories of the world.

As soon as Dasaratha came, Rama and Sita were married. There was great feasting for many days. Then Dasaratha and his three Queens and Rama and Sita and all the lords went back to their own country.

King Dasaratha was getting old. He had been a good king and all his people loved him. He had long trained Rama to take his place. So it was planned that Rama and Sita would become King and Queen.

Now King Dasaratha had three wives, as was then the custom in India. The First Queen was the mother of Rama. The Second Queen was the mother of Lakshmana. The Third Queen was the mother of Bharat.

The Third Queen was young and beautiful. At one time, when King Dasaratha had been wounded in battle, the Third Queen had taken care of him. At that time, the King had said,

"Most beautiful Queen, you have saved my life. Wish for anything that you want. I promise to give you two wishes."

The Third Queen had said,

"My lord, there is nothing that I wish for now."

"When the time comes that you do wish for something," said the King, "I will give it to you."

Now that Rama was to be made king, the Third Queen did wish for something. She came to King Dasaratha and told him. And Dasaratha was very sad.

For the Third Queen had two wishes. Her first wish was that her son Bharat would be made king. Her second wish was that Rama and Sita should be sent away from the country for fourteen years.

The promise of a king cannot be broken. Dasaratha made Bharat king. And he sent Rama and Sita away into the forest. But King Dasaratha never looked again upon the face of his Third Queen.

Lakshmana, the son of the Second Queen, had always loved Rama. He went away with him and Sita.

Soon Dasaratha grew sick and died. And King Bharat, who had never wanted to be king, went into the forest to find Rama. He wanted Rama to come back to his country and to be its king.

Bharat found Rama in the forest. When he asked Rama to become king, Rama said,

"I know, Bharat, that you love me. But I promised my father that I would stay away from my country for fourteen years. I cannot break my promise."

Then Bharat took off the golden sandals that he wore and said,

"Our father wore these golden sandals when he sat upon the throne as king. I will take these sandals back to our country. I will hang them above the throne until you come back and put on the golden sandals of King Dasaratha."

LAITE

Ravana, King of the Rakshasas

There are many stories about Rama and Sita and Lakshmana. They lived in the forest for fourteen years. Rama and Sita were happy because they loved each other very much. And Lakshmana was happy to serve them.

One day, an ugly woman saw Rama and fell in love with him. She tried to get Rama to take her for a second wife. But Rama said that he loved only Sita and would not take a second wife.

Now the ugly woman was the sister of Ravana, King of the Rakshasas. The Rakshasas were wicked giants that killed and ate people.

When Ravana heard about Rama and his sister, he sent his soldiers to kill Rama. But Rama, with his magic bow and arrows, killed all the soldiers but one. This one went back to King Ravana.

"Great King," said the soldier, "no one can kill Rama, for the gods have given him their strength."

"What can I do?" said Ravana.

"Rama has a wife, Sita, who is the most beautiful woman in the world. Rama loves his wife more than his own life. Take Sita away from him and Rama will die."

Ravana went to the Man of Black Magic who lived in a hut outside his castle gate.

"It is with magic that we must steal Sita," said Ravana. "Change yourself into a golden deer with silver spots. Be sure that Sita sees you. Then Rama will try to catch you for her. Lead him far into the forest. While he follows you, I will steal Sita."

The Man of Black Magic changed himself into a golden deer with silver spots. The plan of Ravana worked just as he has said, except that Rama shot the golden deer with one of his arrows.

When the Man of Black Magic, who was the deer, was hurt, he played still one more trick. He called out in a loud voice,

"Sita, Sita. Send Lakshmana to help me."

The voice sounded just like the voice of Rama. Sita heard the voice and was sure that Rama had been hurt. She sent Lakshmana to help him.

Just as soon as Sita was left alone, Ravana appeared. He carried off Sita in his chariot that went up into the sky like a golden cloud. He took her to his castle on the Island of Lanka.

Rama rushed back to the hut in the forest. On the way he met Lakshmana who was coming to help him.

"Why did you leave Sita?" cried Rama. "The King of the Rakshasas has stolen Sita and has taken her to his castle."

Rama and Lakshmana started out to find Sita. But they did

not know where the King of the Rakshasas had his castle.

One day the brothers climbed up to the top of a high mountain. They found a Vulture sitting on the top of the mountain.

"Tell me," said Rama, "have you seen my Sita, the most beautiful woman in the world?"

"One day I saw a Rakshasa fly south through the sky in a golden chariot," said the Vulture. "He had a beautiful woman with him. The beautiful woman was crying.

"The Rakshasas live on the Island of Lanka. There is a beautiful city there, and a castle on a hill. Sita is held in the castle by Ravana, King of the Rakshasas."

Rama and Lakshmana went south into the land of the Monkey People. Thousands of the Monkey People went with the brothers to the ocean. They wanted to help the brothers, but they did not know how to get across the ocean to the Island of Lanka.

Then Hanuman, who was the son of the Wind god and the leader of the Monkey People, said,

"I will call all my people. They will bring rocks and we will make a bridge of rocks over to the Island of Lanka."

Thousands and thousands of monkeys came. They made a bridge of rocks over to the Island of Lanka.

The giant Rakshasas laughed and laughed to see the Monkey People coming over the bridge. A hundred of the biggest giants rushed out of their city to step upon the Monkey People. But the Monkey People were too quick for them. They jumped out of the way and then a hundred monkeys would jump on a giant and kill him. The Monkey People killed all the giants.

When the giants had been killed, Ravana, King of the Rakshasas, came out of his castle to fight with Rama. He made himself as big as a mountain.

All day long Rama and Ravana fought. Never before had there been such a battle. The gods helped Rama and gave him strength. At last Ravana, King of the Rakshasas, lay dead on the ground.

At last Rama and Sita were together again. The fourteen years were almost up. So Rama and Sita and Lakshmana started for their own country.

Hanuman, leader of the Monkey People went with them.

"I can travel much faster than you," said Hanuman. "I will go and tell your brother, Bharat, that you are coming."

For fourteen years Bharat had been keeping the Kingdom of his father, Dasaratha, for Rama. And now everything was ready to make Rama King and Sita the Queen. There was feasting and dancing and everyone was happy.

At last King Rama put on the golden sandals of his father, King Dasaratha, who had ruled his people with such kindness.

"I shall try to be as good a King as my father," said Rama.

There was great happiness in the days that Rama was King.

To this day, in different parts of India, the people act out the Story of Rama. The people wear costumes like our Halloween costumes. There are firecrackers. There is much feasting and dancing. And the people shout, "Victory to Rama. Victory to Rama."

All the children in India know the story of Rama and Sita.

How to Say Some Words from India

The word divided into syllables.	*How to say the word.*
Bha-rat	Bhah-raht
Brah-man	Brah-mahn
Chin-ta-ma-ni	Cheen-tah-mah-nee
Da-sa-ra-tha	Dah-sah-rah-thah
Dur-ga	Door-gah
Ha-nu-man	Hah-noo-mahn
jack-al	jack-all
Ja-na-ka	Jah-nah-kah
Lak-shma-na	Lakh-shmah-nah
Lak-shmi	Lahk-shmee
Lan-ka	Lahn-kah
Ma-ha-ra-jah	Mah-hah-rah-jah
man-go	man-goh
Mi-thi-la	Mee-thee-lah
Ra-jah	Rah-jah
Rak-sha-sa	Rahk-shah-sah
Ra-ma	Rah-mah
Ra-va-na	Rah-vah-nah
ru-pee	roo-pee
Sa-ni	Sah-nee
Shi-va	Shee-vuh
Si-ta	See-tah
Sri-bat-sa	Sree-baht-sah